Walk Around

By Greg Davis and Chris Neill
Color by Don Greer
Illustrated by Richard Hudson

F-18 Hornet

Walk Around Number 18

squadron/signal publications

Introduction

The US Navy and Marine Corps F/A-18 Hornet was originally conceived and built by the Northrop Corporation as the YF-17 Cobra during the 1970s. The YF-17 was designed to meet requirements of the US Air Force's Lightweight Fighter competition — a competition eventually won by the General Dynamics (later Lockheed Martin) F-16 Fighting Falcon.

Despite its apparent failure as a contending USAF fighter, the YF-17 was resurrected to fulfill a US Navy/Marine Corps requirement for a modern, carrier-based fighter and attack aircraft to replace both the McDonnell Douglas F-4 Phantom II and A-4 Skyhawk. McDonnell Douglas was brought into the program since Northrop lacked experience in developing carrier aircraft. Although the YF-17's general configuration remained the same, the aircraft eventually grew into a larger, heavier, and more powerful multi-role fighter and attack aircraft designated the F/A-18 Hornet.

The F/A-18 Hornet has been progressively upgraded over the years and has found itself becoming one of the best and most successful fighter/attack aircraft of the late twentieth century. The US Navy and US Marine Corps have operated six different versions — the F/A-18A through the F/A-18F — both in single and two-seat configurations. New and unique systems have been employed to turn the Hornet into a multi-role combat aircraft capable of finding and striking targets in the air, on land and at sea, during both day and night. The F/A-18 Hornet saw extensive combat during the Persian Gulf War of early 1991 as well as during a series of low-intensity conflicts since then. Additionally, the Hornet has been widely exported — Australia, Canada, Finland, Kuwait, Spain, and Switzerland all have Hornet nests. Following on the heels of its predecessors, the F-4 Phantom II and A-4 Skyhawk, the F/A-18 Hornet will provide outstanding service well into the twenty-first century.

Acknowledgements

NAS Pensacola T-Line personnel
V. Lee Bracken
Jeff Rankin-Lowe/SIRIUS
Gerhard Lang
David F. Brown
Kelly AFB Public Affairs and Transient Alert personnel
NAF Atsugi Public Affairs
Denise Dion/PAX River F/A-18 program Public Affairs
Randy Hepp/USN
Kevin Flynn/Boeing
Ensign Mike Blankenship
Lt. Erick Goss/AIRPAC Public Affairs

Daryl Stephenson/McDonnell Douglas
Aerospace America/Smith & Associates
NASA - Ames Dryden/Public Affairs
Curtiss Knowles
Capt Mike "Homey" Cederholm, VMFA-112
Capt Mick "Sumo" Beckwith, VMFA-112
Maintenance Department, VMFA-112
In addition, we thank the numerous individuals of the Navy and Marines, and all those unmentioned, that assisted us in obtaining information and images for this project. Your tremendous efforts were a valuable asset to the completion of this book.
THANK YOU!

Dedications:

Greg L. Davis would like to dedicate this book to his grandparents, Lt Col and Mrs. Charles I. Davis, (USAF, Ret), for their lifelong inspiration and genuine support.

Chris Neill would like to dedicate this book to his wonderful wife for her encouragement and support unselfishly given to this and all projects. Also to his newborn daughter and a special thanks to his best friend Greg for his dedication, drive, and motivation. Thanks again!

ISBN 0-89747-401-5

If you have any photographs of aircraft, armor, soldiers or ships of any nation, particularly wartime snapshots, why not share them with us and help make Squadron/Signal's books all the more interesting and complete in the future. Any photograph sent to us will be copied and the original returned. The donor will be fully credited for any photos used. Please send them to:

**Squadron/Signal Publications, Inc.
1115 Crowley Drive
Carrollton, TX 75011-5010**

Если у вас есть фотографии самолётов, вооружения, солдат или кораблей любой страны, особенно, снимки времён войны, поделитесь с нами и помогите сделать новые книги издательства Эскадрон/Сигнал ещё интереснее. Мы переснимем ваши фотографии и вернём оригиналы. Имена приславших снимки будут сопровождать все опубликованные фотографии. Пожалуйста, присылайте фотографии по адресу:

**Squadron/Signal Publications, Inc.
1115 Crowley Drive
Carrollton, TX 75011-5010**

軍用機、装甲車両、兵士、軍艦などの写真を所持しておられる方はいらっしゃいませんか？どの国のものでも結構です。作戦中に撮影されたものが特に良いのです。Squadron/Signal社の出版する刊行物において、このような写真は内容を一層充実し、興味深くすることができます。当方にお送り頂いた写真は、複写の後お返しいたします。出版物中に写真を使用した場合は、必ず提供者のお名前を明記させて頂きます。お写真は下記にご送付ください。

**Squadron/Signal Publications, Inc.
1115 Crowley Drive
Carrollton, TX 75011-5010**

(Front Cover) Lt Cdr Mark 'MRT' Fox, of VFA-81, scores the first of two US Navy air-to-air kills during OPERATION DESERT STORM in early 1991. Lt Nicholas 'MONGO' Mongillo of the same unit flamed another MIG-21 seconds later.

(Previous Page) A two-seat TF-18 awaits its crew under cloudless blue skies. Continuing modifications and upgrades will allow the current F/A-18 Hornets to remain a deadly combat aircraft well into the 21st Century. The boarding ladder, which provides access to both cockpits, folds up under the port fuselage Leading Edge Extension (LEX).

(Back Cover) An F/A-18C of VFA-113 awaits its pilot on the deck of the USS CARL VINSON under cloudy dawn skies. After a brief respite, the constant cycle of launchings and recoveries will begin for another 24-hour period.

(Above) The prototype F/A-18, seen here in 1978, was larger and far heavier than the Northrop YF-17. Testing revealed that the landing gear was insufficient to withstand the rigors of repeated carrier takeoffs and landings. A complete redesign of the landing gear and its stowage was necessary to turn the Hornet into a carrier strike fighter.

(Left) The F/A-18 Hornet shares a near identical planform with the earlier Northrop YF-17 — a lightweight fighter designed for the USAF during the 1970s. Turning the YF-17 into a US Navy carrier fighter required expertise that was, in some respects, beyond the capabilities of Northrop. McDonnell Douglas, already experienced in carrier fighter development, was brought in as the prime contractor.

(Below) The fifth full scale development F/A-18, seen here in a blue-and-white test paint scheme, was equipped with the new landing gear required for carrier use. This Hornet was also tasked with the evaluation of avionics and weapon systems and is carrying both the AIM-9L Sidewinder infra-red and AIM-7 Sparrow radar guided air-to-air missiles.

Most of the F/A-18 Hornet airframe is made of aluminum, while the fuselage spine, wing and flap skins, and the vertical fin and stabilator skins are made of a dark colored graphite/epoxy composite material. Steel and titanium are also used in the airframe. All of the materials are combined to build an airframe that is both lightweight and strong.

(Above) The F/A-18 has evolved into a deadly strike fighter capable of engaging both air and ground targets by day or night. This F/A-18A, assigned to VFA-203 Blue Dolphins, carries Multiple Ejector Racks (MER) on each underwing pylon. Each MER can carry up to six practice bombs, but are not normally used in combat.

(Right) The F/A-18 Hornet shares the general planform of the YF-17 Cobra, but has been extensively redesigned in detail. This is a two-seat F/A-18B — also known as a TF-18. It retains the full weapons delivery capability of the single seat F/A-18A. The gun muzzle port and its flanking vents are stained from weapon's firing.

(Below) F/A-18A Hornets are serving with US Navy and Marine squadrons around the world. Other Hornets have been exported to Canada, Europe, the Middle East, and Australia. This Hornet is approaching a USAF KC-10 Extender tanker to take on a load of fuel. (C. Knowles)

5

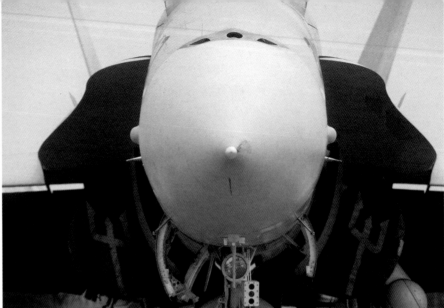

(Above) The tip of the radome on most F-18s is yellow-tan, while the remainder is light gray. The radome is hinged to the starboard of the aircraft which allows access to the Hughes AN/APG-65 multi-mode radar.

(Left) The 20mm M61A1 rotary cannon gun fires through the center port above the radome. Two flanking vents bring cooling air into the gun as well as purge gun gases from the nose compartment. The air is then vented out the lower starboard side of the nose.

(Below) Hornets, like most modern US fighters, are equipped with low voltage formation lighting panels for formation flying under low-light conditions. A pair of covered radar warning receiver antennas are above and below the strip light. At lower left is the circular mounting plate for the angle of attack sensor's air data probe.

(Above) Bronze colored pitot tubes are mounted on both sides of the lower nose. This is the port pitot tube. Directly in front of the nose landing gear are avionics and gun cooling vents. An Ultra-High Frequency/Identification Friend or Foe (UHF/IFF) blade antenna is mounted below the fuselage.

(Right) The Hornet's sting consists of a single 20mm M61A1 Vulcan rotary cannon, motorized drive and feed mechanisms, and a 570 round drum magazine. The entire system is known as the GAU-11. The weapon fires at a rate of 6000 rounds per minute.

(Below) Canadian CF-18 (also known as CF-188) Hornets are equipped with a single high intensity white spotlight mounted in the port side of the nose. The light was added to aid in the identification of targets at night. Cooling holes were added to the panel to vent heat generated by the light.

The lower starboard side of the fuselage contains avionics cooling grids and a bulged cover for the AN/ALR 67 radar warning receiver. This Hornet is also equipped with a false canopy painted on the nose landing gear doors. A blade antenna is offset to starboard behind the wheel well doors.

Avionics bays are located in the lower half of the fuselage to allow easy access without having to use stands or ladders. This is a Canadian Hornet. The Canadian maple leaf insignia and the ARMED FORCES/FORCES CANADIENNES markings surround the insignia.

The radome is hinged to starboard and can be completely folded back along the starboard fuselage side. The Hughes AN/APG-65 multi-mode digital tracking radar slides out of the nose which allows unencumbered access to the entire unit. This Hornet is a CF-188B — the Canadian version of the two-seat F/A-18B Hornet.

AN/APG 65 Multi-Mode Radar

The GAU-11 20mm ammunition loading door is directly below the foremost section of the LEX. The moveable angle-of-attack vane, which measures the Hornet's pitch against the actual line of flight, is mounted on the fuselage side at lower left.

A small hole permits the venting of liquid oxygen (LO2 or LOX). Aft of the LOX vent is a brass colored air temperature sensor probe. This area is on the port side of the fuselage just above the nose gear retraction strut.

An empty avionics bay is used to store the REMOVE-BEFORE-FLIGHT flags and pins. The wiring bundle connectors have been capped to prevent corrosion or damage.

A single point ground refueling receptacle is located on the starboard side above the cooling inlet grills. All of the Hornet's fuel tanks can be filled from this receptacle. The refueling control panel and the crew chief's intercom connection and volume control are also located here.

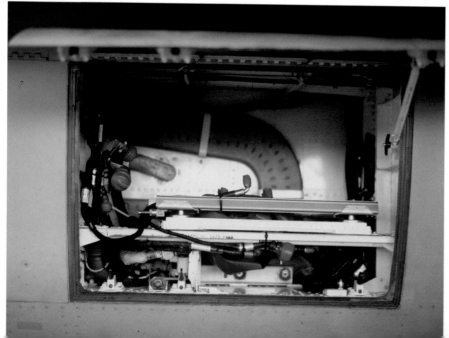

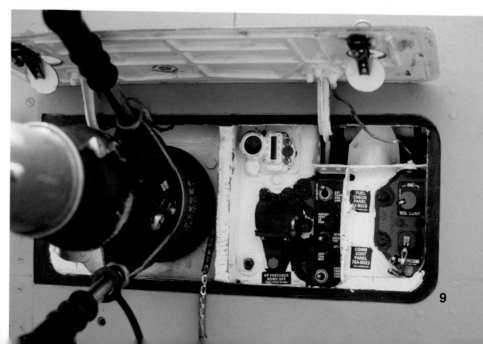

F/A-18Cs on patrol along the Saudi Arabia/Iraq border move into formation with a USAF KC-10 tanker during OPERATION SOUTHERN WATCH in 1993. The Hornets are looking for Iraqi fighters violating the southern no-fly zone. Each Hornet is armed with four AIM-7F Sparrow missiles and a pair of AIM-9L Sidewinder missiles. (C. Knowles)

F-18 Fuel Capacity

Fuselage (four tanks):..................	1,419 Gallons
Wing (one tank per wing):.............	170 Gallons
Centerline Drop Tank:....................	330 Gallons
Port Wing Drop Tank:....................	330 Gallons
Starboard Wing Drop Tank:...........	330 Gallons
Total:..............................	2612 Gallons

The F/A-18 can carry approximately 1600 gallons (10,400 lbs) of internal JP-4 fuel, while the three external tanks can add another 990 gallons (6435 lbs). Both internal and external fuel tanks can be filled using the single point pressure refueling system port mounted within the starboard side of the aircraft nose just aft of the radome.

10

A heavily stained and weathered F/A-18C approaches a USAF tanker to receive fuel during May of 1992. Hornets are only clean when they first deploy. During extended carrier operations, emphasis is placed on keeping them combat ready — not pretty. (C. Knowles)

An F/A-18A approaches a tanker to take on a load of fuel. The refueling probe cover door, just to starboard of the gun muzzle, is beginning to open. Also visible are the three angled brackets used to reinforce the vertical fin to fuselage joint on the F/A-18A. Buffeting caused by air flowing around the Leading Edge Extensions (LEXs) led to premature fatigue cracking in the fin/fuselage joint. The cracking problem was solved when these brackets were added on the assembly line and retrofitted to earlier Hornets. Later, small fences were added to the LEXs to smooth out the airflow. Later production F/A-18Cs had internal stiffeners added to the fin/fuselage joint and eliminated the external brackets. This Hornet is carrying a Multiple Ejector Rack (MER) on the port outer wing pylon. MERs are normally used to carry light practice bombs. Standard iron bombs, ranging from 500 to 2000 lbs each, are carried on a Vertical Ejector Rack (VER). Each VER carries two bombs and up to five racks can be carried by an F/A-18. (C. Knowles)

An F/A-18C approaches a USAF KC-10 from directly behind. The pilot has activated the refueling probe which is beginning to open. (C. Knowles)

An armed F/A-18C of VFA 94 formates on a tanker while waiting for its turn to refuel. The refueling probe is in the fully open position. The Hornet pilot will fly the probe into a basket trailing from a hose reeled out of the tanker. (C. Knowles)

An F/A-18C pilot eases into position behind a KC-10. Once contact is made, the probe and basket will lock together and fuel will begin flowing into the Hornet's tanks. The probe light housing is visible at the base of the probe. (C. Knowles)

The refueling probe and the interior of its cover are painted red, while the probe well is primarily white. A small white light is mounted at the base of the probe to assist in night refueling.

Fuel flow begins once the probe and drogue are locked together. The probe light is mounted in the small white housing at the base of the probe's retraction strut. (C. Knowles)

Radar and Refueling Probe

All F/C-18 Hornets are capable of aerial refueling using the probe-and-drogue aerial refueling system. The probe is offset in the upper starboard section of the nose where it is in full view of both the F-18 pilot and tanker boom operator. This is a Canadian CF-188A assigned to 425 Squadron, Canadian Forces Base (CFB) Goose Bay, Labrador.

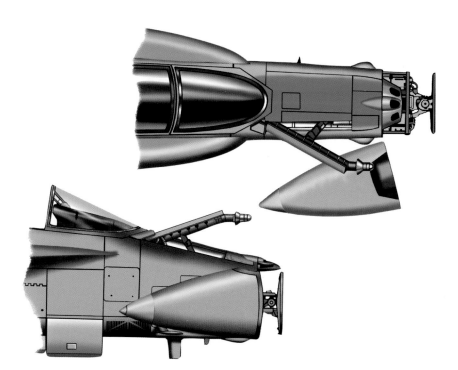

13

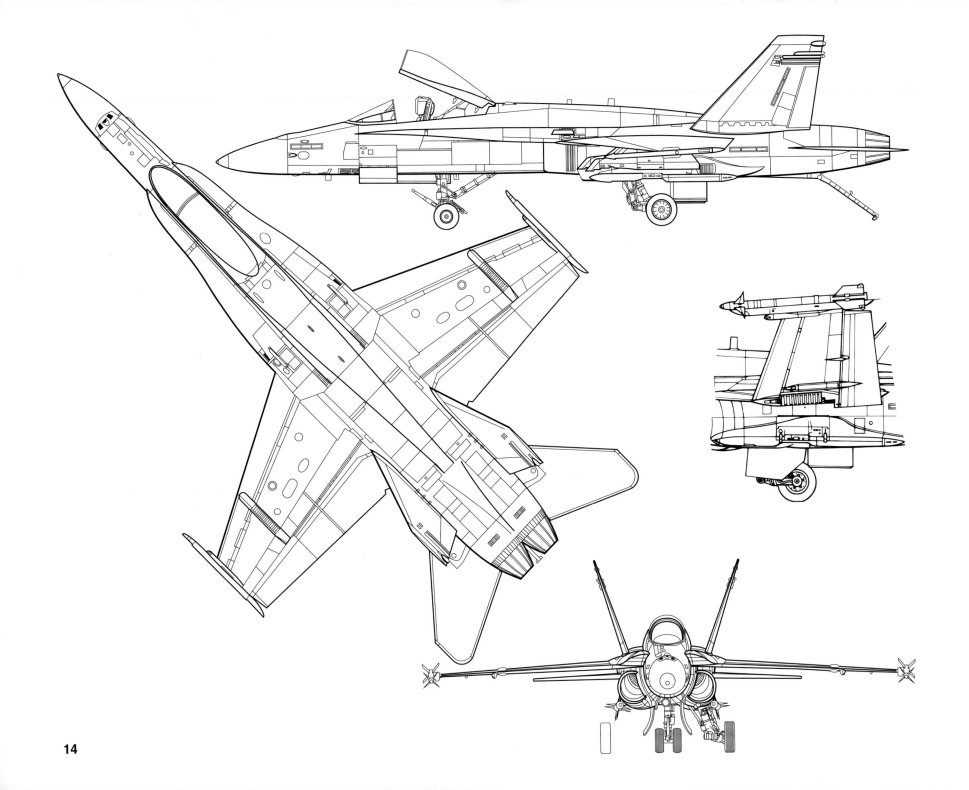

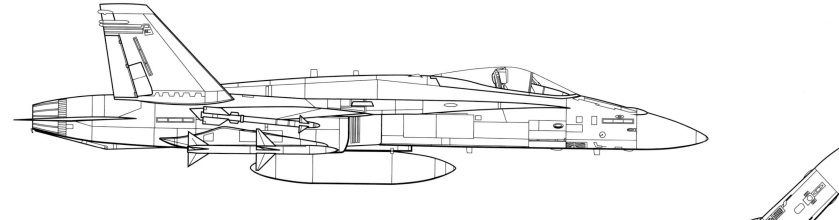

F-18C Specifications

Wingspan:..............37 feet, 6 inches (11.43 m) (w/o
                          launchers)
Length:...................56 feet (17.06 m)
Height:...................15 feet, 3.5 inches (4.66 m)
Weight (Empty):....23,000 lbs (10,433 kg)
Weight (Combat):..Up to 51,900 (23,541 kg)

Powerplant: Two x GE F404-GE-400 turbofan engines w/
approximately 16,000 lbs thrust each (later F404-GE-402
engines produce 17,600 lbs thrust)

Armament: One x 20mm M-61 rotary cannon w/ 570
rounds
External Stores: Unguided bombs/rockets, precision
guided bombs, air-to-air and air-to-surface missiles

Max Speed:..............1122 mph (1805 kmh)
Ceiling:....................50,000 feet (15,240 m)
Range (Unrefueled w/ three ext tanks):
                          Approximately 2000 miles
                          (3219 km)

Crew: One

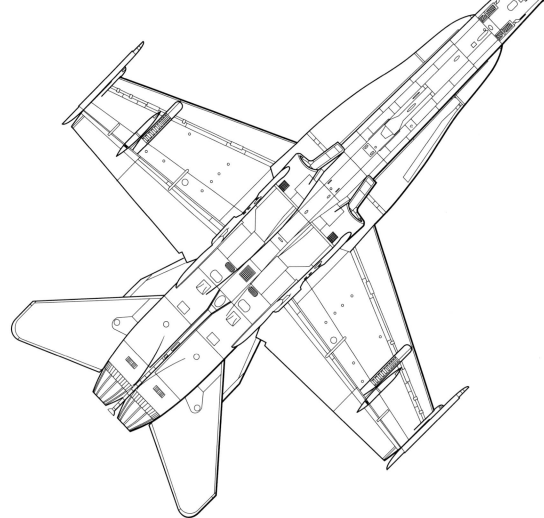

Two F/A-18Cs taxi out with their full length leading and trailing edge flaps in the down position. The leading and trailing edge flaps are used for both takeoff and landing. Additionally, the flaps are used in combat to improve maneuverability.

The engine intakes are separated from the fuselage by a fixed splitter plate which is braced at both the top and bottom. The wedge shape behind the plate is designed to direct air through the LEX slot above and over the fuselage and down around the lower fuselage. An air intake for the air conditioning and cabin pressurization system is incorporated into the point of the wedge.

A heavy wire cage is placed over the intakes during ground engine tests to prevent the ingestion of foreign objects. These objects, and the damage they can cause, are collectively known as FOD (Foreign Object Damage) throughout the US military. Visible atop the LEX is a small vertical fence — designed to improve the airflow around the vertical fin, reduce buffeting, and thereby prevent metal fatigue. A green navigation light is built into the starboard LEX.

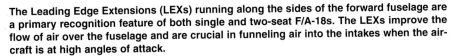

The Leading Edge Extensions (LEXs) running along the sides of the forward fuselage are a primary recognition feature of both single and two-seat F/A-18s. The LEXs improve the flow of air over the fuselage and are crucial in funneling air into the intakes when the aircraft is at high angles of attack.

(Above) A strake (or fence) was added to the LEX to improve air flow around the aft fuse-lage and vertical fins. A red navigation light is incorporated into the port LEX. The TACAN aerial and the larger UHF-IFF antenna are mounted on the fuselage spine.

(Right) Most of the intake trunking is painted gloss white to allow ground crews to easily spot foreign objects or leaks.

(Below) Two cooling air spill vents are mounted adjacent to the port LEX strake.

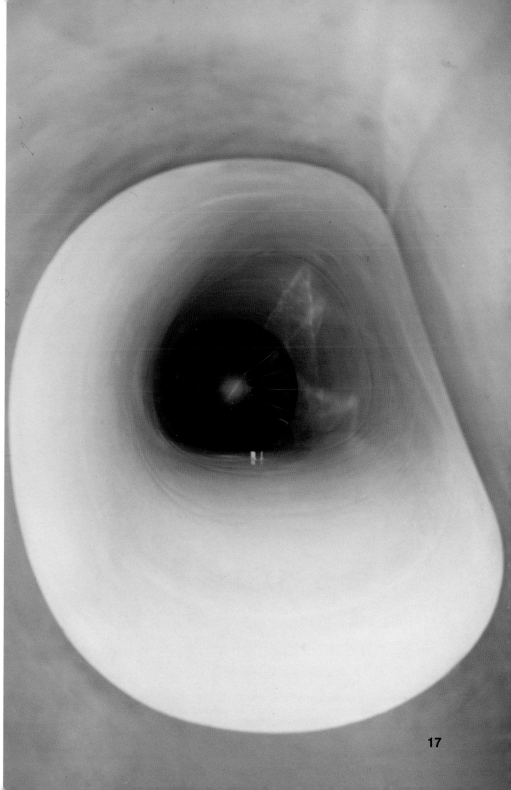

An aircrew boarding ladder is incorporated into the underside of the port LEX. The ladder is manually raised and lowered by the ground crew and is braced against the fuselage by a V-shaped strut. The ladder serves both cockpits on the two-seat Hornet.

The aircrew boarding ladder is stored in a shallow, white painted well under the port LEX. The support strut is fastened into a socket on the fuselage side.

The intake weapons hardpoints are each equipped with a pair of push rods that function as sway braces as well as pushing ordnance — such as an AIM-7 Sparrow AAM — away from the fuselage.

An AN/AAS-38 Forward Looking Infra-Red (FLIR) pod is mounted on the port fuselage weapons station. The forward section of the pod is moveable in several axis which allows the imaging sensor to maintain a lock on the target. The pod transmits a real-time daylight-like image of the target onto the Multi-Function Displays (MFD) and Head-Up Display (HUD) in the cockpit.

An AN/ASQ-173 Laser spot tracker and camera (LST/CAM) pod is mounted on the starboard intake station when the F/A-18 is configured for air-to-ground missions. (C. Knowles)

The AN/ASQ-173 LST/CAM tracks a laser spot used to target Laser Guided Bombs (LGBs). The strike camera then records the results of the strike. Many pods require special adapters when they are attached to the intake stores stations. (C. Knowles)

19

(Above) The nose gear bay is enclosed by four doors — one each to port and starboard which enclose the wheel bay, one to starboard which encloses the main strut bay, and one fastened to the retraction strut which encloses the retraction strut well. A yellow servicing placard is attached to the interior face of the main strut bay door. Additionally, each door is edged in red as a safety warning. The catapult launch bar is raised and lowered via the cylindrical unit behind the strut and just above the tires.

(Left) The F/A-18 Hornet is equipped with a massive, fully steerable, twin wheel nose landing gear. The landing light is mounted at the top of the strut. Immediately below the landing light is the box containing the three carrier approach attitude indicator lights. A carrier launch bar is mounted on the front of the strut. The launch bar is hydraulically lowered to engage the catapult shuttle.

(Above) The nose gear retraction strut pushes the vertical strut forward into the nose gear well. The nose gear tires are 22 inches in diameter and are pressurized to 350 psi for carrier operations. The catapult launch bar hydraulic unit is mounted behind the strut above the tires and torque links.

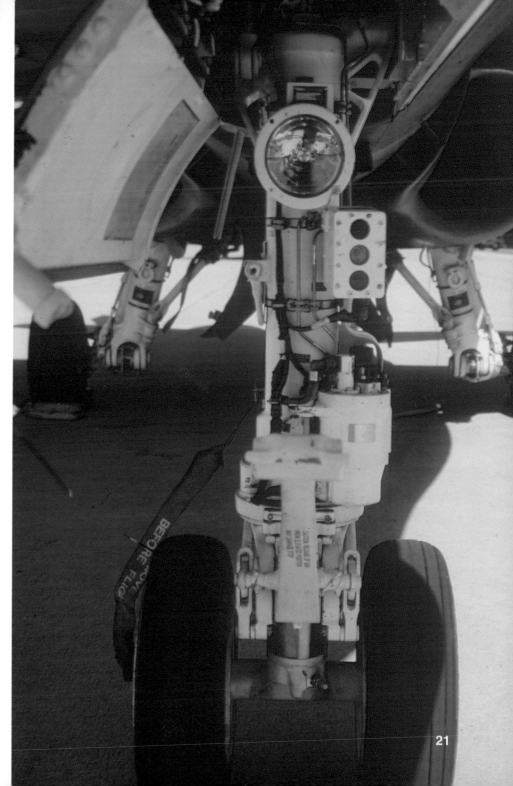

(Right) The large cylindrical housing above the port tire is the hydraulic steering unit. The nose wheel unit can be steered up to 75° left or right using a combination of control stick switches and the rudder pedals. A landing light is mounted at the upper portion of the nose gear strut, while the approach attitude indicator lights are mounted in a box offset to port.

(Above) The catapult launch bar, here in the raised or landing position, is attached to the front of the main gear strut. It can be hydraulically lowered to engage the catapult shuttle imbedded into the catapult track. (C. Knowles)

(Left) The port and starboard wheel well doors are opened and closed using a pair of door retraction struts. The starboard wheel well door is linked to the starboard strut well door allowing both doors to be drawn closed using a single retraction strut. Only a few inches separate the aft gear door from the front of the 330 gallon centerline fuel tank.

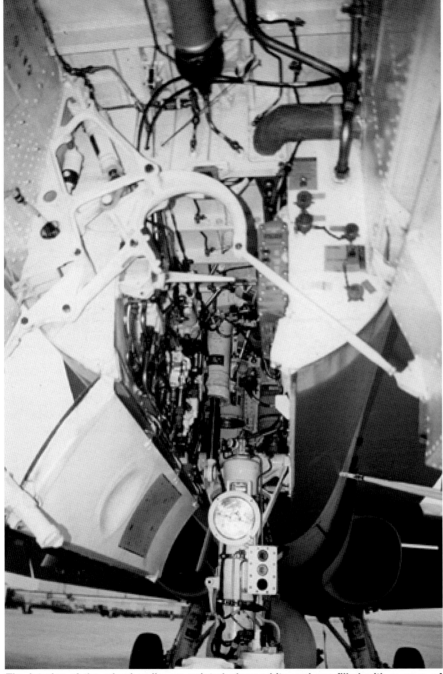

The interior of the wheel wells are painted gloss white and are filled with a maze of hydraulic service lines for the nose gear retraction system, steering, catapult launch bar, and wheel well door activation. The white paint allows the groundcrews to easily spot hydraulic leaks.

When the aircraft is on jacks, the nose gear oleo extends to its full length. The oleo functions as a large shock absorber to cushion the effects of carrier landings — or not so soft ground landings. (G. Phillips)

(Above) The landing gear on this Swiss Air Force F/A-18 has been completely retracted, but the gear doors have yet to close. The nose gear retracts straight forward, however, the main gear retracts aft and pivots 90˚ to allow the single main gear tires to lay flat within the wheel well. (Mather Benoit)

(Above Left) The nose-gear can be steered up to 75˚ left or right which allows the Hornet to almost pivot in place — a valuable capability when on the tight confines of a carrier deck. Steering is controlled using a combination of the rudder pedals and electrical switches on the stick.

(Left) A Canadian CF-18A rolls inverted to display its underside while the landing gear is half way through its retraction sequence. The landing gear and wheel wells are painted gloss white. The heavily stained aft fuselage contrasts sharply with the subdued grays of the remainder of the airframe. Canadian Hornets are officially designated CF-188, however, both designations are used on an equal basis.

Bronze-colored Bendix disc brakes are barely visible through the lightening holes in the main wheel. Both the wheel and landing gear struts are painted white. An AN/ASQ-173 Laser Spot Tracker/Strike Camera (LST/CAM) pod is mounted on the starboard fuselage weapons station.

Hydraulic lines for the braking system snake down the main strut, along the trailing beam, and into the Bendix disc brakes mounted on the inner surface of the wheel. A tie-down ring is mounted on the aft section of the main strut, while another is mounted on the front half.

The vertical main strut and the horizontal trailing axle beam are connected by a single shock absorber. The tires are 30 inches in diameter and pressurized up to 350 psi for carrier operations.

The lower aft fuselage section contains vents, the Auxiliary Power Unit (APU) exhaust, and the main landing gear bays. Forward of the wheel bays is the centerline 330 gallon drop fuel tank.

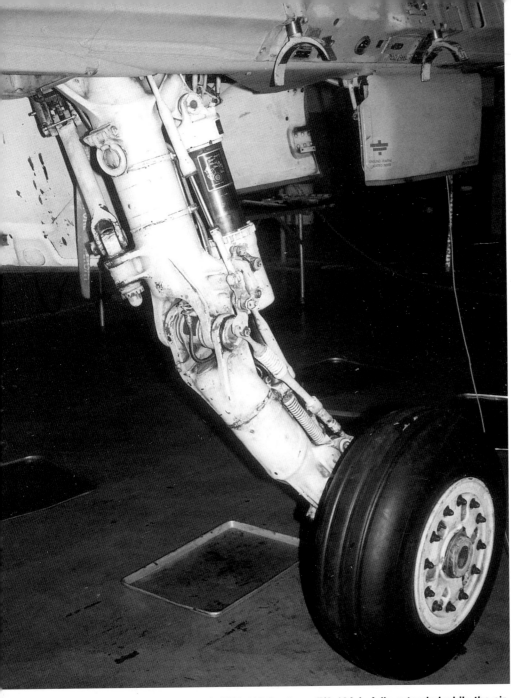

The main landing gear of this VFA-112 Cowboys F/A-18A is fully extended while the aircraft is up on jacks. Hydraulic rams retract the gear, while another pivots the strut 90° to fit within the well. (G. Phillips)

The landing gear struts are made of steel and designed to withstand the forces involved in repeated carrier deck landings. Maintenance data placards are attached to the oleo shock absorber to aid groundcrews. (G. Phillips)

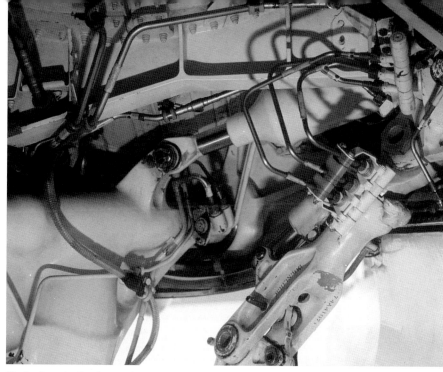

Tucked up in the forward section of the strut well is the main gear retraction ram. The assembly is surrounded by a maze of hydraulic service lines.

The main landing gear of this F/A-18 has been considerably cleaned up for a public air-show. A tie down ring is mounted on the upper section of the main strut. (C. Knowles)

A system of hydraulically activated arms and struts open and close the wheel well doors. The landing gear retraction ram is attached to the top of the main vertical strut. A diagonal bracing strut is attached to the lower end of the main strut and runs up to the opposite side of the gear well.

27

(Above) The landing gear is retracted almost immediately after takeoff. The nose gear retracts forward, while the main gear begins its aft retraction and 90° rotation cycle.

(Above Left) An F/A-18D flares out in ground effect (a cushion of air squeezed between the aircraft and the ground) just prior to touch down. The fuel tanks are mounted forward on the notched pylons to provide clearance for the flaps on take-off and landing. The tanks can be retained for some combat operations, but are usually jettisoned for any combat involving hard maneuvering.

(Left) Tire smoke billows up behind the wheels when they go from zero to over 125 knots on landing. The nose gear strut of this F/A-18D is fully extended while the pilot holds the nose off the runway to take advantage of aerodynamic braking. Aerodynamic braking uses a high angle of attack to expose more of the airframe to the slip stream and slow the aircraft down. F-18s are not equipped with drag chutes.

(Above) The F/A-18 has a single curvature windshield with a frameless molding. The frameless, yet high impact resistant windshield provides excellent forward visibility and increased pilot safety. The windshield and instrument panel shroud hinges up and forward to provide access to the Head-Up Display (HUD) and the front side of the instrument panel.

(Above Right) Single seat Hornets are equipped with a one piece, aft-hinging canopy. Three mirrors and two grab handles are normally mounted on the front canopy bow. The interior canopy frames are painted flat black to reduce glare. (C. Knowles)

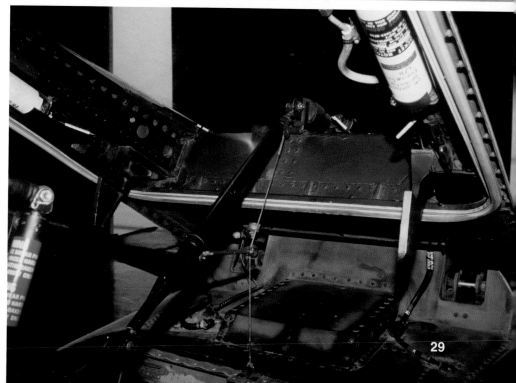

(Right) The canopy is raised and lowered via a single rod connected to the rear of the canopy frame. The hooks engage catches in the cockpit sill to hold the canopy securely in place. (G. Phillips)

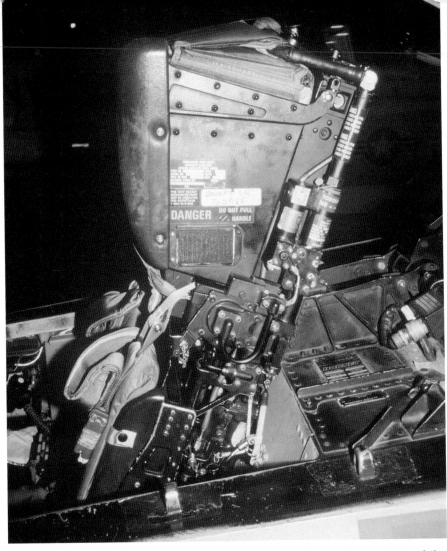

(Above) The Martin-Baker SJU-5A Ejection Seat is located immediately in front of the canopy raising mechanism. The seat is painted a semi-gloss black. Hornets use the SJU-5 and SJU-6 ejection seats — both are similar and differ only in minor details. (G. Phillips)

(Above Left) The lower end of the canopy jack is connected to a pivoting bell-crank attached to an electric motor. (G. Phillips)

(Left) A pair of hinges connect the canopy to the airframe. The rear decking is painted flat black, however the well behind the seat is painted light gray. The well is often covered with a fine net to prevent objects from falling into the well. (G. Phillips)

(Above) The AN/ALR-67 RHAW scope (on top) provides the approximate range and bearing of air or ground-based threat emitters such as a MiG-29 Fulcrum radar or an SA-6 Gainful surface-to-air missile radar. Different symbols are used to depict the threat emitters. The rings are used to approximate range, while the clock position tick marks provide a bearing. The AN/ALR-67 panel (below) is used to control the system. The system provides visual and aural warning only, but has no jamming capability. But, forewarned is forearmed... (Mick Roth)

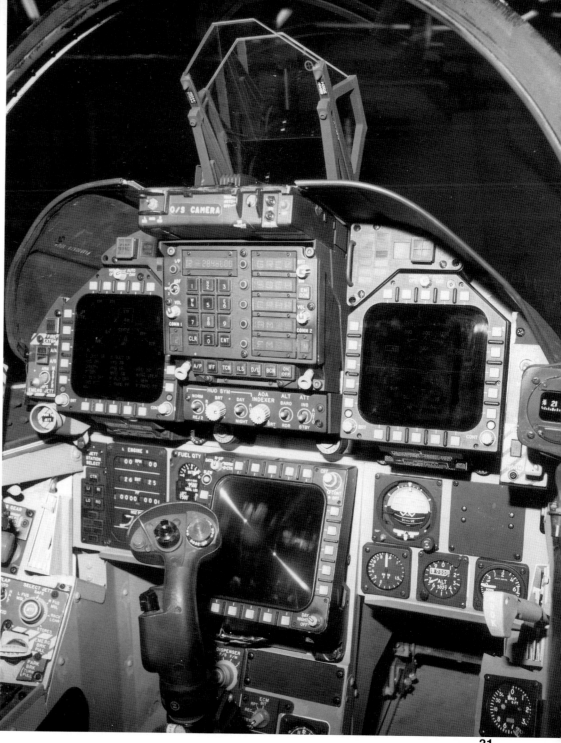

(Right) The F/A-18A instrument panel is dominated by three large Multi-Function Displays (MFD) which provide a variety of systems, navigation, and targeting data to the pilot. Much of this information can be repeated in the Head-Up Display (HUD) mounted on top of the instrument panel shroud. The square blanking plate at right covers the hole left by the removal of the AN/ALR-67 Radar Homing and Warning (RHAW) scope, while the rectangular plate at the bottom covers the space for the RWR control panel. (McDonnell Douglas via Mick Roth)

The Multi-Function Displays provide aircraft systems operation, navigation, and targeting data to the pilot through-out the course of an F/A-18 mission. Analog instruments provide additional information or function as a back-up to the MFDs. (G. Phillips)

A digital control panel is mounted in the top center of the instrument panel. A numerical keypad is placed to the left, while digital readouts are mounted to the right. This panel is used to control various radio navigation aids, as well as enter navigation waypoint information. (G. Phillips)

The lower left portion of the instrument panel contains the fuel quantity gauge and a panel containing rolling digits for (top to bottom) engine RPMs, Exhaust Gas Temperature, and Fuel Flow. Below these are the exhaust nozzle position and oil pressure indicators. (G. Phillips)

The right MFD is mounted under a fiberboard shroud which covers the entire upper surface of the instrument panel. This MFD displays navigation and flight data. A back-up compass is mounted on the windscreen frame at right. (G. Phillips)

A secondary analog instrument cluster is mounted directly beneath the right MFD. The panel contains an Attitude Reference Indicator (ARI), a taped over RWR scope, an airspeed indicator, an altimeter, and vertical speed indicator. All, but the RWR scope, are backups to the displays in the MFDs. (G. Phillips)

33

(Above) The engine throttles are mounted on the port console. Bristles prevent objects, such as a pen, from falling into the slots and jamming the mechanism. (M. Beckwith)

(Above Left) Both left and right consoles sweep up to meet the lower corners of the main instrument panel. A third panel extends down the center to the floor and divides the foot wells to the rudder pedals. (G. Phillips)

(Left) The starboard console contains environmental and lighting controls and a cockpit light. The canopy activation switch is mounted in the gray box under the sill and in front of the cockpit light. (G. Phillips)

The stick is centered in the cockpit in front of the seat. The stick grip and center portion are black, while the lower portion is gray. The ejection seat is fired using the center yellow and black pull ring. The round window in the left forward portion of the seat is an inspection port. (G. Phillips)

The stick contains buttons to control aircraft trim, weapons selection, release/firing, sensor skewing, and autopilot and nosewheel steering functions. (G. Phillips)

(Above) A Forward Looking Infra-Red (FLIR) control panel is mounted on the starboard console just behind the environmental and lighting controls. The yellow-striped handle on the ejection seat is a manual override, while the yellow loop next to the seat cushion releases the survival kit. (Mick Roth)

(Left) Footwells flanking the center console contain the rudder pedals. The rudder pedals are normally painted gray, but are quickly scuffed to a natural metal appearance. (G. Phillips)

(Below) Switches for the Auxiliary Power Unit (APU), the aerial refueling probe, and various pieces of communications equipment are located aft of the throttle quadrant. (M. Beckwith)

(Above) The pilot's G-suit connection and oxygen controls are mounted at the extreme aft end of the port console. (M. Beckwith)

(Above Right) Both throttles can be gripped with one hand. Switches for the radar, speed-brake, chaff and flare dispensers, and some targeting functions are mounted on the hand-grips. The pilot can fly and fight the Hornet with his hands solely on the stick and throttle — a concept known as Hands On Throttle And Stick (HOTAS) (M. Beckwith)

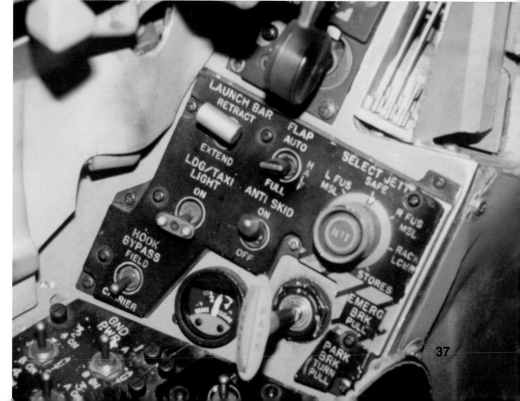

(Right) The emergency and parking brake handle is located on the forward port console. Additional controls include the launch bar and stores jettison controls. A brake pressure gauge is centered in the lower portion of the panel. (M. Beckwith)

Two-seat Hornets use an elongated version of the single seater's canopy to allow access to the aft cockpit. A reinforcing bow is incorporated across the center of the canopy.

The canopy has two hinges along its rear edge — this is the starboard hinge. A built-in clamp grabs the horizontal retaining bar when the canopy is closed. Additional hooks are mounted along the canopy side rails.

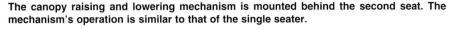

The canopy raising and lowering mechanism is mounted behind the second seat. The mechanism's operation is similar to that of the single seater.

The upper portion of the canopy raising and support rod is centered at the aft end of the canopy and is visible beneath the canopy. The entire canopy can be jettisoned in an emergency.

(Above) Two-seat Hornets, such as this F/A-18D, have multiple canopy frame locks which run the length of each canopy rail. The canopy is fitted with hooks which lock into receptacles incorporated into the cockpit sills.

(Right) The longer canopy of the two-seat Hornet is broken only by a central reinforcing frame in the middle. A lightweight reinforcing spar was added across the lower frame to provide additional structural rigidity. Both single and two-seat canopies maintain a near 360° view.

(Below) The canopy hooks are fastened into the canopy rail. The entire interior surface of the canopy is normally painted flat black to reduce glare.

The front cockpit of two-seat F/A-18s is virtually identical to that of the single seaters. The pilot is provided with three large MFDs and analog back-up instruments. The Head-Up Display (HUD) dominates the instrument panel shroud under the single-piece windscreen. TF-18s and F/A-18Ds are equipped with both SJU-5 and SJU-6 ejection seats. The two seats are almost identical, differing only in minor details. This is the front cockpit of an F/A-18D. The cockpit walls and floor are generally painted gray, while the modular components of the instrument panel and consoles and the seat are flat black. Safety and emergency related controls are usually yellow — often with black stripes.

The large panel above is used to control and input data into the three multi-function displays. Most of the controls in the front cockpit are identical to those found in the single seat F/A-18s. One exception is the fuel and engine monitoring panel (below) mounted in the lower left portion of the instrument panel. F/A-18As and TF-18s use analog gauges, however, the F/A-18C and F/A-18D are both equipped with electronic displays.

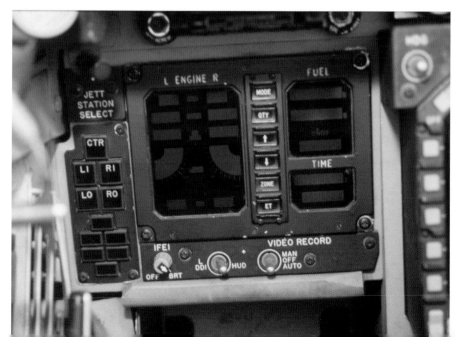

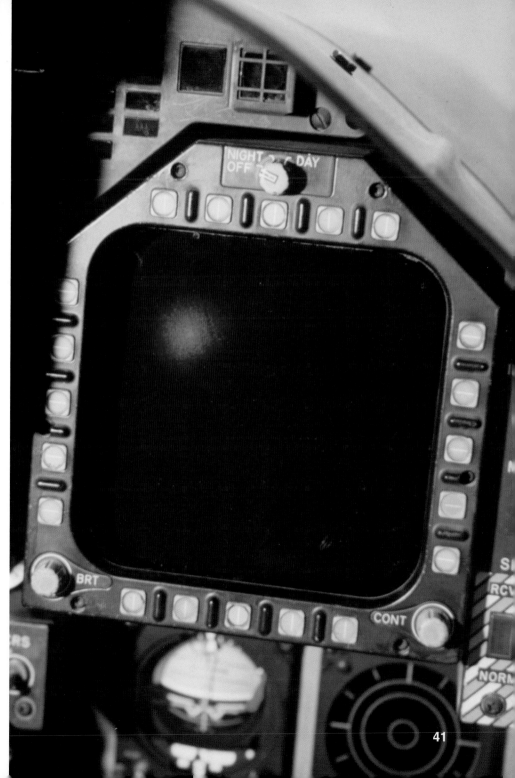

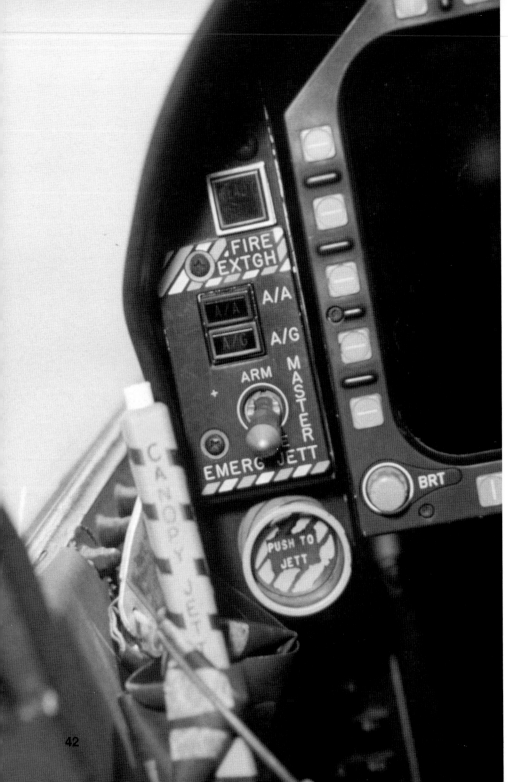

Two seat F/A-18s retain the full combat capability of the single seat Hornets, consequently the front cockpit instrumentation reflects this capability. The EMERG(ency) JETT(ison) switches allow the pilot to quickly release his external stores in the event of an emergency. The lower right portion of the instrument panel (above) retains the earlier AN/ALR-67 RHAW scope. F/A-18Cs and Ds were supposed to receive an internal tactical warning and jamming system (AN/ALQ-165), but these were not fitted due to budgetary constraints. The TF-18, the two seat version of the early F/A-18A, is most often used in the training role, however, F/A-18Ds have evolved into deadly night attack strike fighters.

Both engine throttles are normally moved together unless one engine is inoperative. The handles are small enough for the pilot to grip both throttles with his left hand, while still using his thumb and fingers to activate the assorted switches on the throttle sides and front. The rudder pedals are coated with a rough, non-skid surface. Footstraps, common on WW II fighters, are not used since the pilot's feet must quickly come off the pedals in the event of an ejection. The red-handled landing gear control is located on the front vertical portion of the port console.

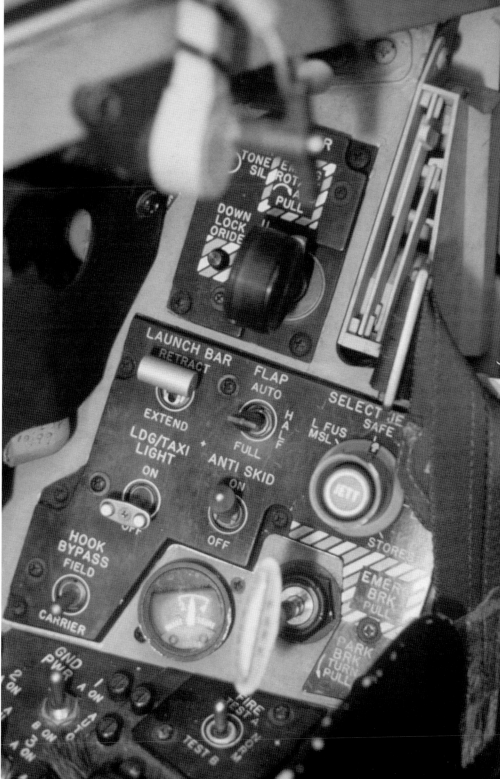

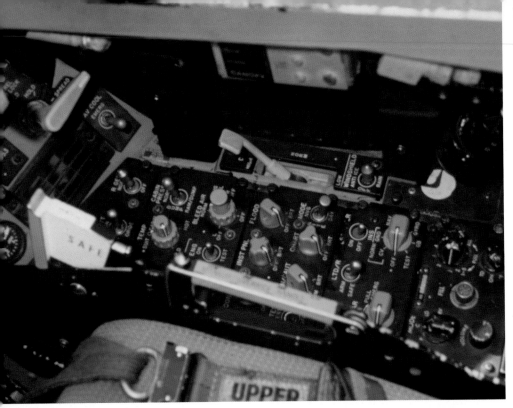

The predominate color of the cockpit structure is gray. Some areas are covered with a gray quilted insulated padding. Instrument and control boxes are normally flat black and covered with gray plastic knobs and natural metal switches. Much of the cockpit gradually takes on a worn, scuffed appearance. The starboard console contains controls for the environmental (air conditioning and heating) and aircraft lighting system, FLIR and LST/CAM pods, and the Identification, Friend or Foe (IFF) system. The small plug labeled FILL towards the rear (right) of the panel at upper left is used to feed coded data into the Hornet's IFF system.

F/A-18B/D Canopy

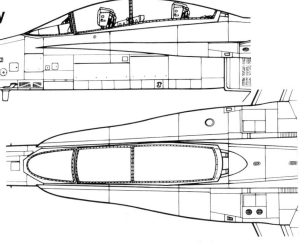

The Kaiser manufactured Head-Up Display (HUD) employs two plates of optically flat glass. The HUD is used to display both weapons release, navigation, and aircraft attitude data.

HUD data is projected up through the circular lens and onto the glass plates. A small video camera is used to record data projected onto the HUD. HUD video was widely released to the news media during OPERATION DESERT STORM in early 1991.

The pilot has a clear, unobstructed view through the HUD and over the nose. An angle-of-attack/stall warning indicator is mounted on the left side of the HUD mounting frame. This indicator provides the pilot with a visual stall warning, while an aural tone sounds in his headphones.

The HUD is mounted on top of the instrument panel shroud. The pilot can navigate and fight the Hornet using HUD data and the stick and throttle controls.

The HUD provides aiming points for both air-to-air and air-to-ground weapons. The HUD can display data from the AN/APG-65 multi-mode radar and the internal bombing computer. Both systems will also tell the pilot when to release or fire his weapons.

The aft cockpit is equipped with most of the instrument panel displays of the front cockpit, however, their arrangement can be different. Additionally, TF-18s are normally dual-controlled, while F/A-18Ds lack the stick and throttle controls and substitute sensor and weapons guidance controls in their place. F/A-18Ds can be converted back to dual control if necessary.

The control stick in the front cockpit is identical to that found in the single seat F/A-18A and F/A-18C. The left button on the top of the stick is red. Like the throttles, the stick grip is covered with a variety of switches used to fly and fight the Hornet — all part of the HOTAS concept.

The aft cockpit seat is higher than the front cockpit seat. The higher seat provides an improved field of vision for the Naval Flight Officer (NFO) occupying the rear cockpit and operating the weapons and sensors. The NFO, also known as the GIB (Guy in Back), is not provided with a HUD.

All F/A-18s are equipped with SJU-5/A or SJU-6/A series ejection seats. These seats are also known as NACES, or Naval Advanced Concept Ejection System, seats. The 18-foot diameter parachute is stored in the headrest. This parachute has a higher rate of descent over the larger diameter parachutes used by the USAF.

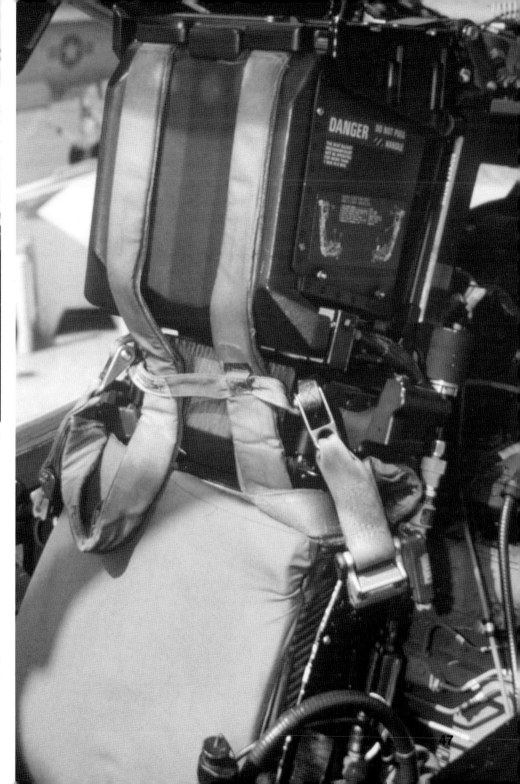

The front cockpit of this Canadian CF-18B is overall gray, while the instrument panel, side consoles, and individual instruments are black. The interior frame of the windscreen is also black to reduce glare. The cockpit is generally identical to those found in US Navy and Marine Hornets (J. Rankin-Lowe)

The single and two-seat F/A-18s use a combination of the Martin Baker SJU-5/A or SJU-6/A NACES (Naval Advanced Concept Ejection System) ejection seats. All are similar in design and operation, but differ in some small details. This is the SJU-5A (Modified) seat found in the aft cockpit of the Canadian CF-18B. (J. Rankin-Lowe)

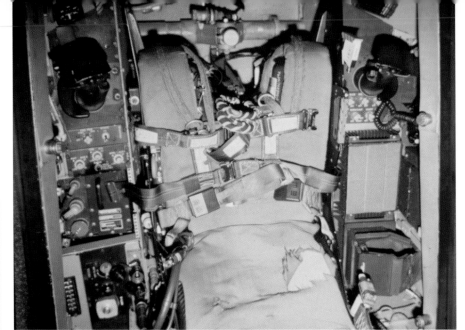

F/A-18D Hornets are fully combat capable and have a variety of special capabilities — especially the Night Attack Hornets. This F/A-18D is equipped with weapons and sensor control handles on both the port and starboard cockpit sides. These aircraft retain the capability of being returned to dual-control. The base of the control stick mount is visible just in front of the seat. (M. Roth)

The aft cockpit F/A-18D Night Attack Hornet is similar to the front cockpit with the exception of the primary flight controls: the stick and throttle. The three MFDs are spread across the top of the instrument panel rather than having the center display mounted on the lower section. An additional set of indicator lights and switches has been added across the top of the panel directly beneath the shroud. The ejection seat pull ring has been covered with a bag to prevent inadvertent activation.

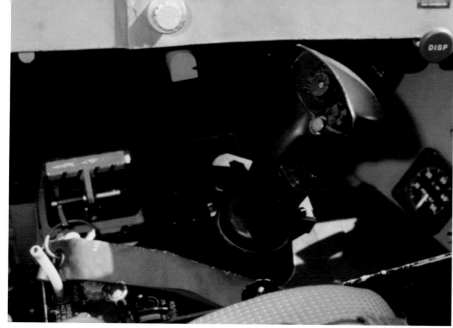

(Above) The port console grip controller (above) and starboard controller (below) are used to provide guidance for air-launched air-to-ground munitions — such as laser-guided bombs — and maintain a target lock by one of the sensor/designator pods carried by the Hornet.

(Right) The central MFD has changed places with the indicator and keypad panel used on earlier Hornets. Additionally, the new center MFD is a full color display which provides a better image of both targets or built-in electronic maps. Visible in front of the seat is the covered socket for a control stick.

(Below) The starboard grip controller is used in conjunction with the port controller to maintain a target lock for the Hornet's weapon's guidance systems.

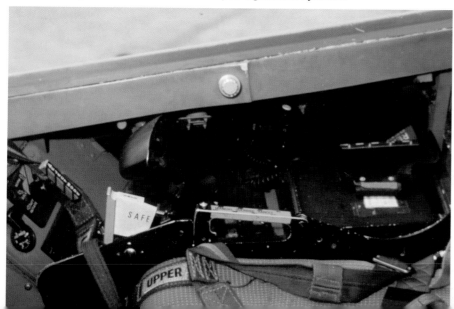

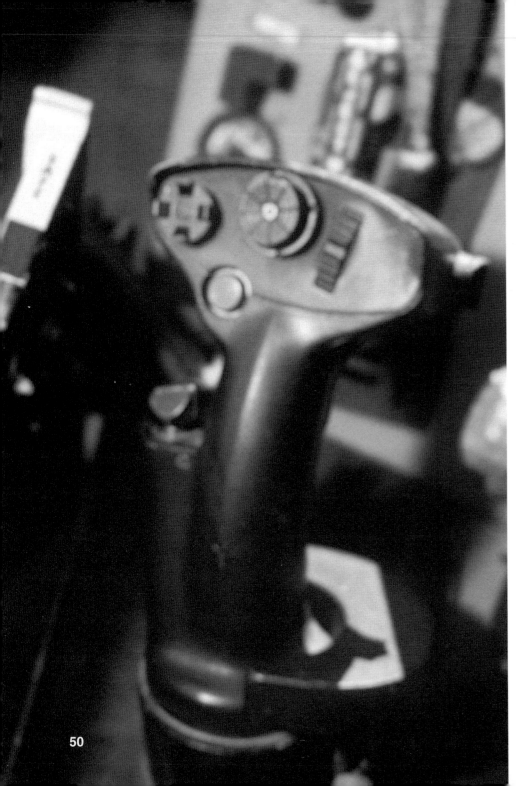

(Above) The aft portside console contains a memory module for an on-board computer. Further aft is the chaff and flare dispenser quantity panel.

(Left) Side console control grips are used to provide sensor tracking or weapons guidance. This is the starboard controller in the aft cockpit of an F/A-18D.

(Below) Chaff and flares are used to counter radar guided and infra-red threats respectively. A small panel located at the extreme aft end of the port console tells the NFO how much of these defense aids are remaining. Chaff and flares are dispensed via the AN/ALE 39 Chaff/Flare Dispensers located on the lower surfaces of the F/A-18.

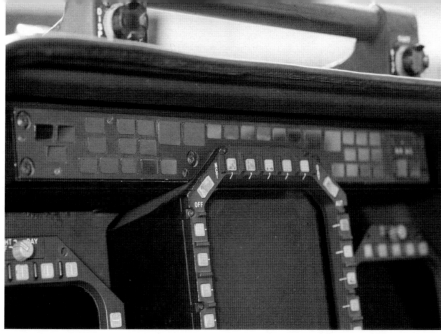

(Above) The upper portion of the F/A-18D aft cockpit contains an additional strip of threat indicator lights and switches. The gray buttons surrounding the MFDs are used to control or activate certain flying, navigation, and targeting functions.

(Right) A hand grip is mounted across the top of the back seat instrument panel shroud. The NFO can use the grip as a lever to turn his body when under high G maneuvers. A second pair of eyes looking out behind can be a life saver in combat.

(Below) The starboard console vertical panel contains the ejection seat controls. Each seat can be fired individually or dual ejection can be initiated by the pilot (front seater) or the NFO. When dual ejection is selected, the back seat is fired first no matter who initiated the ejection sequence.

51

The NFO uses a combination of the Multi-Function Displays and the side console controllers to perform his duties of target acquisition and weapons guidance. The NFO's grab bar is mounted above the instrument panel.

Basic flight instruments and an AN/ALR-67 Radar Homing and Warning scope are repeated on the lower right quadrant of the instrument panel. The upper left instrument is the Attitude Reference Indicator (ARI) — also known as an Attitude and Direction Indicator (ADI), The ARI tells the pilot(s) if they are banking, climbing, or diving.

Martin-Baker
SJU-5/6 Series Ejection Seat

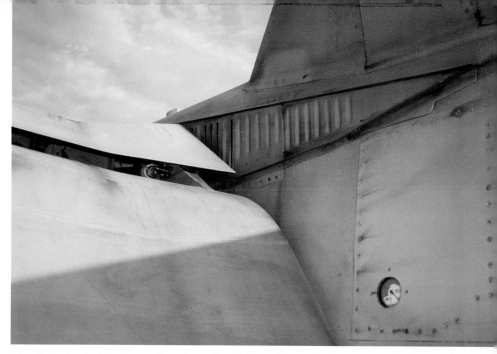

The smooth, if somewhat stained, lines of the Hornet are evident once the landing gear is retracted and the gear doors are closed. This Canadian CF-18 carries a centerline pylon, but lacks the four wing pylons.

The flaps and ailerons occupy the entire trailing edge of the wing. The flaps droop up to 45° for landing. The ailerons, also known as flaperons due to their dual function, provide roll control and act in concert with the flaps to provide additional lift at high angles of attack — a vital element in carrier landings.

Directly in front of the low voltage formation light and just aft of the port side flap is an engine lubrication indicator which allows both the crew chief and flight crew to monitor engine lubrication functions.

Flaps (inboard) and ailerons (outboard) are incorporated into the wing trailing edge. The ailerons can be drooped 45° in concert with the flaps to facilitate carrier landings. The flaps can also be lowered up to 20° during combat maneuvers. The larger antenna on the fuselage spine is the UHF/IFF antenna, while the smaller unit is the TACAN aerial.

(Above) A single large fairing covers the aileron actuators and inboard hinges beneath each wing. A second, smaller external hinge is located further outboard adjacent to the wing tip. This is the underside of the port wing.

(Left) The Hornet employs both internal and external flap hinges and actuators. This actuator is inboard on the starboard lower wing surface.

(Below) A red navigation light is incorporated into the leading edge of the port aileron actuator fairing. The light is only visible from the side or front. The starboard wing fairing contains a blue-green light.

(Above) The wing tip hardpoints are designed to carry a single AIM-9 Sidewinder AAM. During exercises or test flights, the hardpoints can also mount an Air Combat Maneuvering Instrumentation (ACMI) pod on the missile rail. The surface of the wing is slightly bulged to accommodate the wing fold mechanism.

(Right) The leading and trailing edge control surfaces are split to allow the wings to fold. The outer wing panels fold upward to 90° to facilitate carrier stowage.

(Below) The port wing tip hardpoint has a red navigation light built into the front tip of the unit.

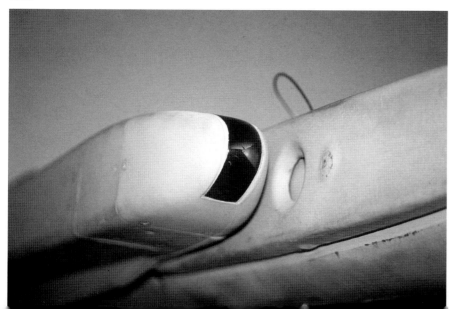

(Above) Both wing tips incorporate a hardpoint for mounting an air-to-air missile launch rail. The face of the starboard hardpoint contains a blue-green formation light. The missile launch rail is fastened to the hardpoint and the missile, in turn, is mounted onto the rail.

(Above Left) The wing tip is folded using a piano hinge. The hinge and its ancillary components are incorporated within a bulge in the upper and lower wing surface. Fuel leaking from the vents beneath the wing has stained the paint.

(Left) The missile rail is angled slightly downwards to accommodate the Hornet's slight nose up cruising attitude. Night formation lights — sometimes referred to as 'slime lights' due to their bright yellow-green color — are mounted on small fences above and below the wing tips. The word 'FIST' on the LEX fence refers to VFA-25 being known as the *Fist of the Fleet*.

(Above) The leading edges of the flying surfaces are made of titanium. The leading edges are sometimes painted dark gray (FS 35237), while the remainder of the upper surfaces are painted Dark Ghost Gray (FS 36320).

(Above Right) The F/A-18 is equipped with three hardpoints on each wing — two under the wing and one on the wing tip. This inboard starboard wing pylon carries a 330 gallon drop tank. The same tank can also be used on the fuselage centerline station. All four wing pylons have a stepped front end to allow the leading edge flaps to droop for takeoff, maneuvers, and landing.

(Right) An F/A-18C taxis slowly forward with both leading and trailing edge flaps drooped. The wing and intake store station are empty, however, a single 330 gallon drop tank is mounted on the aircraft centerline.

The wing pylons can be quickly up or down loaded and can carry a variety of weapons. The inboard pylons are 'wet-plumbed' to carry fuel tanks as well. The aerodynamic shape is light-weight, yet strong enough to carry several thousand pounds — a fully loaded drop tank weighs slightly over 2800 lbs.

The wing pylons are designed to carry a variety of multiple and triple ejector racks as well as special adapters for air-to-surface missiles and other 'smart weapons'. Sway braces are incorporated into the pylon and rack assembly to hold the external ordnance securely in place during high speed maneuvers.

A fuel tank mounted on the starboard inboard pylon underwing station. Wing tanks use a second attachment point on the aft end of the tank. The attachment secures the tail end of the tank to the aft end of the pylon. The stepped leading edge of the pylon allows the leading edge flaps to deflect downward to their full 30°.

The AGM-88 HARM missile is designed to home in on the energy given off by ground or ship-based radars. It is capable of detecting and guiding on most of the radar frequencies in use today without having to pre-program the missile seeker. The missile has a range of approximately 12 miles and carries a warhead weighing some 145 lbs.

This F/A-18C was assigned to VFA-87 Golden Warriors in June of 1996. The Hornet is carrying three 330 gallon fuel tanks — one under the fuselage and one on each inboard wing pylon. The Hornet carries a total of 990 gallons, or 6435 pounds, of external JP-4 fuel.

An F/A-18 is refueled by a USAF tanker. A 330 gallon drop tank is mounted on the inboard pylon, while two AIM-9L Sidewinder air-to-air missiles are mounted on the outboard pylon. The AIM-9L is an all-aspect missile capable of detecting and locking onto targets from behind or in front using thermal energy reflected or emanated from the target. The missile has a range of approximately 10 miles and carries a 21 lb warhead. (C. Knowles)

The rear half of the F/A-18 seems to be one continuous line of flying surfaces: the wing trailing edge leads to the vertical fin leading edge, while the fin trailing edge leads into the horizontal stabilator leading edge. The vertical, slab-sided appearance of the aft fuselage contrasts sharply to the smoothly flowing lines and curves of the forward half of the airframe. (C. Knowles)

A vent is located at the rear of the fuselage weapon station just below the flaps. The entire weapon station is contoured to improve aerodynamics both around the fuselage and the weapon. Controlling the air flow around the stores station and weapon is important to ensure a clean separation when the weapon is launched or released.

The flaps, rudders, and horizontal stabilators are computer controlled to provide maximum flight performance under varying conditions. A red anti-collision beacon is mounted on the outer face of each vertical fin.

The graphite/epoxy speed brake can be quickly deployed to slow the Hornet both in the air and on the ground. Holding the nose off the ground — not an option on carrier landings — also slows the aircraft down via the use of aerodynamic braking.

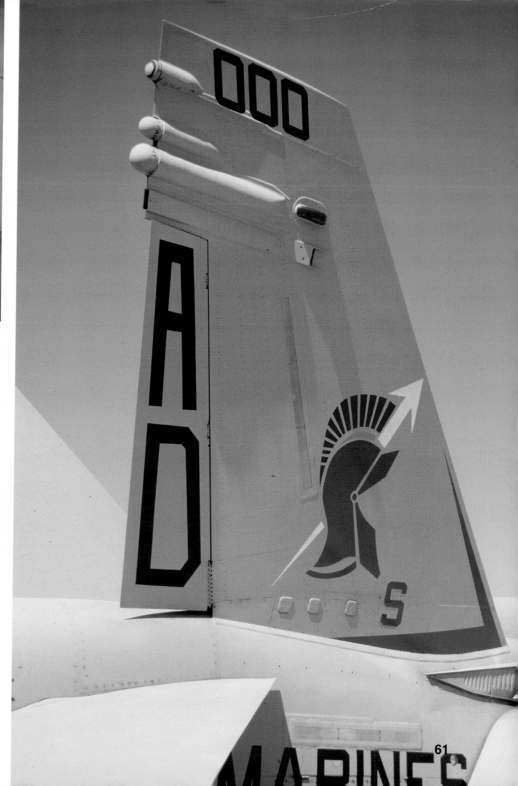

(Above) A low voltage formation strip light dominates the area in front of the horizontal stabilizer on the rear fuselage. Black markings indicate the degrees of movement for the horizontal stabilizer while gray markings indicate the owner — the Canadian Forces — in both English and French.

(Right) The rudders are attached to the vertical fins using three hinges and are actuated using a combination of hydraulics and mechanical linkages. A formation strip light is mounted on the aft fuselage skin between the wing and stabilator.

(Below) The inner face of the upper tail fins contains additional strengthening strips for the glass-fiber fin tips. Both vertical fins are equipped with a rectangular fuel dump port which allows fuel to be dumped up and away from the engine exhaust plumes.

The vertical fins are built using metal spars skinned with graphite/epoxy exterior panels and a titanium leading edge. The fin also serves as a canvas for the Hornet's unit of assignment — Navy Fighter/Attack Squadron 192 (VFA-192), the unit's two-letter code (NF), the assigned aircraft carrier (USS Independence), and the Modex number (300).

The upper section of the port vertical fin is identical to the starboard fin with the exception of the AN/ALQ-165 high band antenna fairing mounted at the top in lieu of the white navigation light.

The arresting hook is marked in two shades of gray. The steel shoe placed on the end of the hook is responsible for catching and holding the arresting wire in place as the aircraft comes to a sudden stop.

The hinge is a universal joint which allows a degree of lateral as well as vertical movement.

The L-shaped hook on the arrestor hook shaft holds the hook in the up position. The black rubber sleeve next to the hook serves as a bumper to eliminate metal-to-metal friction when the arrestor hook is stowed. The arrestor hook is lowered using a combination of gravity and an actuator ram. The ram also functions as a damper to keep the hook down.

(Above) F/A-18s routinely carry external fuel tanks, since the Hornet has a reputation for being a thirsty and short-legged fighter. Drop fuel tanks and aerial refueling contribute substantially to the Hornet's range and loiter time.

(Left) The twin vertical fins on the F/A-18 Hornet are canted outward to improve stability. The outward angle is a marked contrast to the twin vertical fins of the USAF F-15 Eagle. The rudders can be toed inward to provide additional braking.

(Below) The GE-F404 engine exhaust nozzles are equipped with 12 hydraulically actuated outer flaps, or petals. These are used to provide optimum thrust for varying conditions. The nozzle at right is in the fully closed position, while the nozzle at left is slightly open. Both can be fully open when higher thrust is required.

(Above) The interior of this almost fully opened exhaust nozzle reveals the sooty white appearance of the afterburner interior. The rear face of the engine is visible through the afterburner section. This is a GE F404-GE-402 engine with ceramic faces on the petals.

(Right) Panels covering the lower rear fuselage can be removed to facilitate engine maintenance and removal. The port and starboard engine bays are separated by a titanium wall. The wall functions as a 'scatter shield' in the event one engine suffers catastrophic failure and starts throwing turbine parts. The wall prevents thrown parts from damaging the remaining engine.

(Below) Both engines can be easily removed from the F/A-18's rear fuselage section. Most of the engine accessories are attached to the engine and are removed at the same time. The interior of the engine bay is painted white to improve lighting and help spot leaks.

A two-seat F/A-18D Hornet undergoes pre-flight systems checks. The engines have been powered up and the speed brake, tail hook, refueling probe, and catapult launch bar are all in the deployed position.

An F/A-18A rests on the flightline with its wings folded and canopy up. A tow bar is attached to the nose wheel axles. The leading and trailing edge flaps droop without power to the control systems. The black and white striped hoses of an underground refueling system are visible beneath the Hornet's tail.

A brightly colored F/A-18A of VMFA 321 is parked on the flightline. The 00 on the nose, VMFA 321 on the fuselage side, and the vertical fins are painted dark blue, while the fin stars are white and the 00 and MG are dark red. Hornets are normally painted in a two-tone gray tactical camouflage, however, Navy regulations are believed to allow one or two aircraft to be brightly marked for morale and display purposes.

The US Navy operates Hornets in the aggressor role — this Hornet is painted to resemble a Russian-built MIG-29 Fulcrum. Black paint has been used to represent the Fulcrum's wedge-shaped intakes under the LEX and the auxiliary intakes on top of the LEX. Additionally, gray paint is used to alter the profile of the wing and vertical fin tip.

VFC-12 operates this F/A-18A in the aggressor role. The light and dark gray paint scheme, combined with the black and white shapes on the nose, LEXs, and vertical fins, is designed to emulate the MIG-29 Fulcrum.

Canada operates several squadrons of single and two-seat CF-18s. They are virtually identical to those Hornets operated by the USN and USMC. This CF-18 was assigned to the 3rd Wing and was photographed at the WILLIAM TELL weapons meet in 1994. Canadian Hornets are normally equipped with a large white spot light on the port side of the forward fuselage, however, this aircraft has had its light removed and replaced by a solid panel.

The rebuilt Kuwaiti Air Force operates two squadrons of F/A-18C and D fighters. Kuwaiti Hornets feature a wrap-around scheme of three shades of gray. One of the gray shades has a distinctive tan cast under certain lighting conditions. Kuwaiti AF Hornets are equipped with the more powerful GE F404-GE-402 engine. This engine, also being retrofitted to USN and USMC Hornets, is equipped with ceramic faces to the interior of the exhaust petals.

The Swiss Air Force operates a number of F/A-18Cs from their mountain valley air bases. Swiss Hornets wear a two-tone gray camouflage scheme similar to that of USN and USMC Hornets. The Swiss AF insignia consists of the white cross superimposed over a red disc.

The US Navy Blue Angels aerial demonstration team chose the Hornet due to its high performance and reliability. Solo #5 pulls a hard turn which generates a substantial amount of water vapor off the wing tips and leading edge extensions.

This Canadian CF-18A wears a stylized porcupine paint scheme in honor of the unit mascot. The aircraft was stationed at CFB (Canadian Forces Base) Bagotville in August of 1993.

This F/A-18C Hornet is carrying a pair of AGM-88 HARMs (High-Speed Anti-Radiation Missiles) designed for use against ground-based radars, such as those associated with Early Warning (EW) or surface-to-air missile (SAM) sites. A special adapter is used to attach the HARM to the inboard wing pylon.

This heavily stained and weathered Hornet wears the red and yellow roundels of the *Ejercito del Aire* (the Spanish Air Force). Spanish AF Hornets are designated EF-18 — the E standing for España. The glowing red dot on the LEX is a port navigation light. A second red light is barely visible on the port wingtip missile launching rail.

The Kuwaiti Air Force received F/A-18 Hornets shortly after the 1991 Persian Gulf war. The F/A-18s are used in both the air defense and strike roles. This aircraft is on a test flight before delivery, but is wearing the KAF disruptive paint scheme of three shades of gray.

An *Ejercito del Aire* (Spanish AF) EF-18 goes vertical under the thrust of its two F404-GE-400 afterburning low-bypass turbofan engines. Each engine produces approximately 16,000 pounds of thrust. Spain operates two squadrons of EF-18s: Ala 12 and Ala 15. Both squadrons are equipped with single and two seater Hornets.

Hornet development is not finished. McDonnell Douglas and the Navy are developing the enlarged F-18E and F Super Hornet. This F-18F, the first two seater, takes off carrying a load of inert 500 pound Mk 82 low drag bombs. At least one bomb has been painted with camera reference markings to record its separation characteristics.

The single seat F-18E is longer, has a greater wingspan, and has revised LEXs and intakes. The Super Hornet will gradually replace the aging Grumman (now Northrup Grumman) F-14 Tomcat in US Navy squadrons beginning in 2001.

The first F-18F takes off for a test bomb dropping flight during early fall of 1998. The new Hornets share a general arrangement with the earlier Hornets, but are larger, heavier, and have improved performance and weapons delivery capabilities.

The more powerful and deeper breathing GE F-414 turbofan engine required revised intakes under the leading edge extensions. The round intake and trunking has given way to a box shaped inlet.

(Above) The rear fuselage speed brake on the F/A-18A through D has been deleted and replaced by smaller speed brakes mounted on the upper surface of each LEX.

(Right) The F-18E/F Hornets retain their aerial refueling capacity. The refueling probe is largely unchanged from the earlier Hornets. Fuel capacity is some 33% greater than that of the F/A-18C. Additionally, the new Hornet is able to carry 480-gallon drop tanks to further increase its range and endurance. The nose landing gear design remains similar to that of the earlier Hornets.

(Below) The speed brakes are hinged at their forward edge. The speed brake well also serves as an exit point for bleed or boundary air.

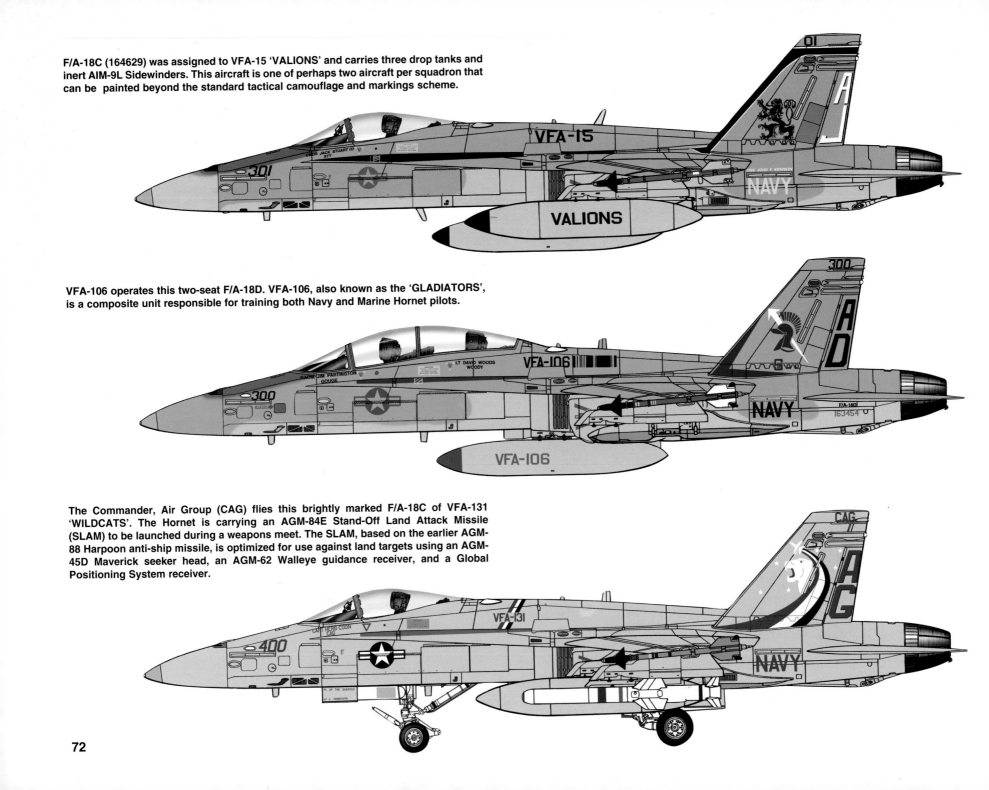

F/A-18C (164629) was assigned to VFA-15 'VALIONS' and carries three drop tanks and inert AIM-9L Sidewinders. This aircraft is one of perhaps two aircraft per squadron that can be painted beyond the standard tactical camouflage and markings scheme.

VFA-106 operates this two-seat F/A-18D. VFA-106, also known as the 'GLADIATORS', is a composite unit responsible for training both Navy and Marine Hornet pilots.

The Commander, Air Group (CAG) flies this brightly marked F/A-18C of VFA-131 'WILDCATS'. The Hornet is carrying an AGM-84E Stand-Off Land Attack Missile (SLAM) to be launched during a weapons meet. The SLAM, based on the earlier AGM-88 Harpoon anti-ship missile, is optimized for use against land targets using an AGM-45D Maverick seeker head, an AGM-62 Walleye guidance receiver, and a Global Positioning System receiver.

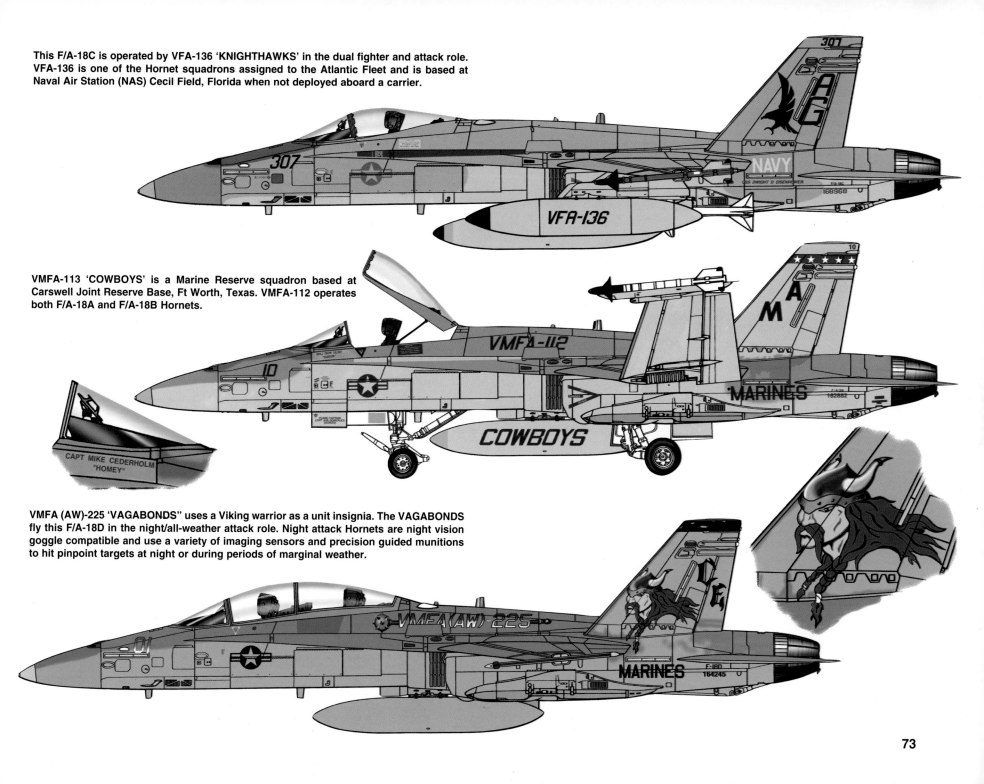

This F/A-18C is operated by VFA-136 'KNIGHTHAWKS' in the dual fighter and attack role. VFA-136 is one of the Hornet squadrons assigned to the Atlantic Fleet and is based at Naval Air Station (NAS) Cecil Field, Florida when not deployed aboard a carrier.

VMFA-113 'COWBOYS' is a Marine Reserve squadron based at Carswell Joint Reserve Base, Ft Worth, Texas. VMFA-112 operates both F/A-18A and F/A-18B Hornets.

VMFA (AW)-225 'VAGABONDS" uses a Viking warrior as a unit insignia. The VAGABONDS fly this F/A-18D in the night/all-weather attack role. Night attack Hornets are night vision goggle compatible and use a variety of imaging sensors and precision guided munitions to hit pinpoint targets at night or during periods of marginal weather.

(Above) The refueling probe and the interior face of its cover door are painted gloss red, while the probe well is white. A small white light is mounted at the base of the probe — a carryover from the earlier F/A-18A through D. The 20mm gun port has been plated over on this aircraft.

(Left) The cockpit layout is similar to the earlier Hornets as well, however, there are now four Multi-Function Displays mounted on the main instrument panel. The new F-18E/F also retains the NACES ejection seats.

(Below) The general design of the one piece windscreen has been retained from the earlier Hornets, however, some revisions have been made to the HUD mounting frame.

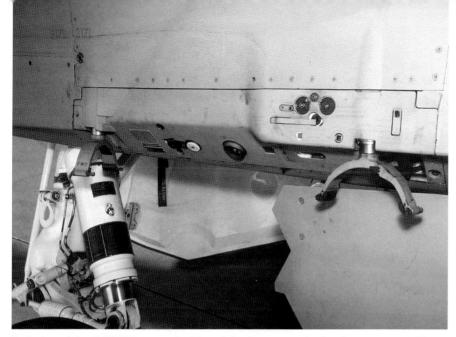

Redesign of the F-18E/F has resulted in subtle changes to the fuselage contours. These changes have resulted in increased internal volume and a lowering of the Super Hornet's radar signature. The portside weapon push-rods are located just above the main landing gear. The rods assist in pushing a missile away from the aircraft once fired.

F-18E/F Hornets retain the general design of the main landing gear used on the earlier Hornets, however, the gear door design has been altered with stealth characteristics to lessen the fighter's radar return. The sawtooth edges are designed to scatter incoming radar waves.

The Super Hornet uses a similar heavy duty, trailing link design on the landing gear. The wheel design has changed, but the earlier 30-inch high pressure tires are retained.

The landing gear has been strengthened to handle the increased weight of F-18E/F Super Hornet. Both main landing gears retract aft and pivot 90° to lay flat within the wheel well.

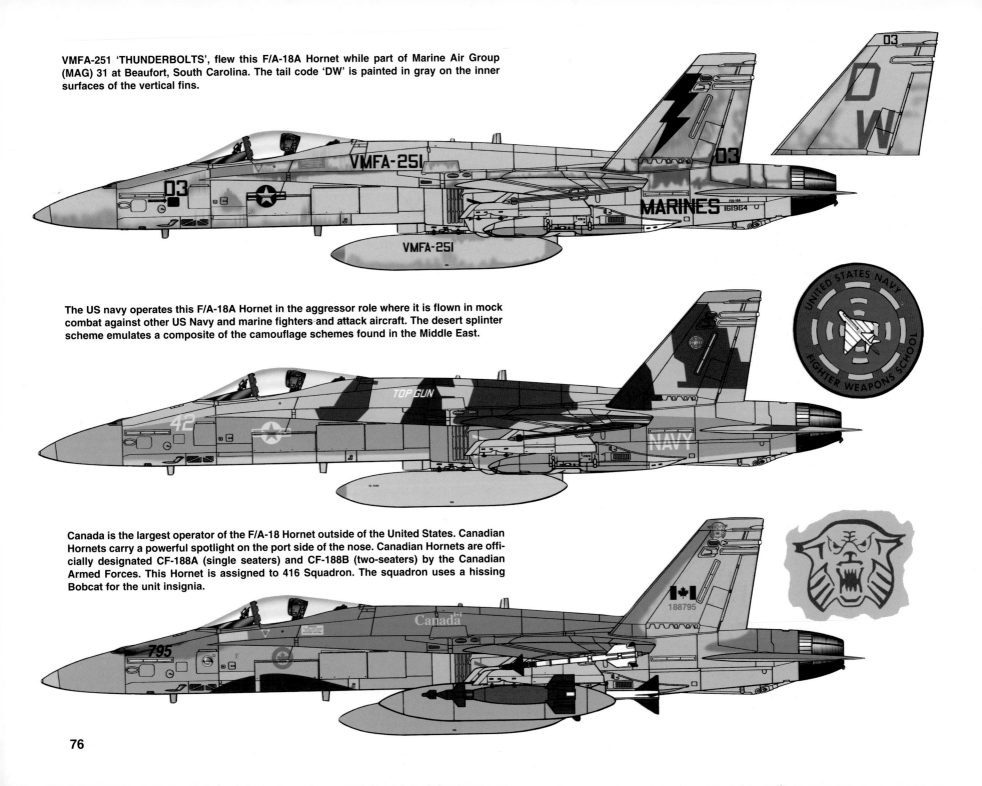

VMFA-251 'THUNDERBOLTS', flew this F/A-18A Hornet while part of Marine Air Group (MAG) 31 at Beaufort, South Carolina. The tail code 'DW' is painted in gray on the inner surfaces of the vertical fins.

The US navy operates this F/A-18A Hornet in the aggressor role where it is flown in mock combat against other US Navy and marine fighters and attack aircraft. The desert splinter scheme emulates a composite of the camouflage schemes found in the Middle East.

Canada is the largest operator of the F/A-18 Hornet outside of the United States. Canadian Hornets carry a powerful spotlight on the port side of the nose. Canadian Hornets are officially designated CF-188A (single seaters) and CF-188B (two-seaters) by the Canadian Armed Forces. This Hornet is assigned to 416 Squadron. The squadron uses a hissing Bobcat for the unit insignia.

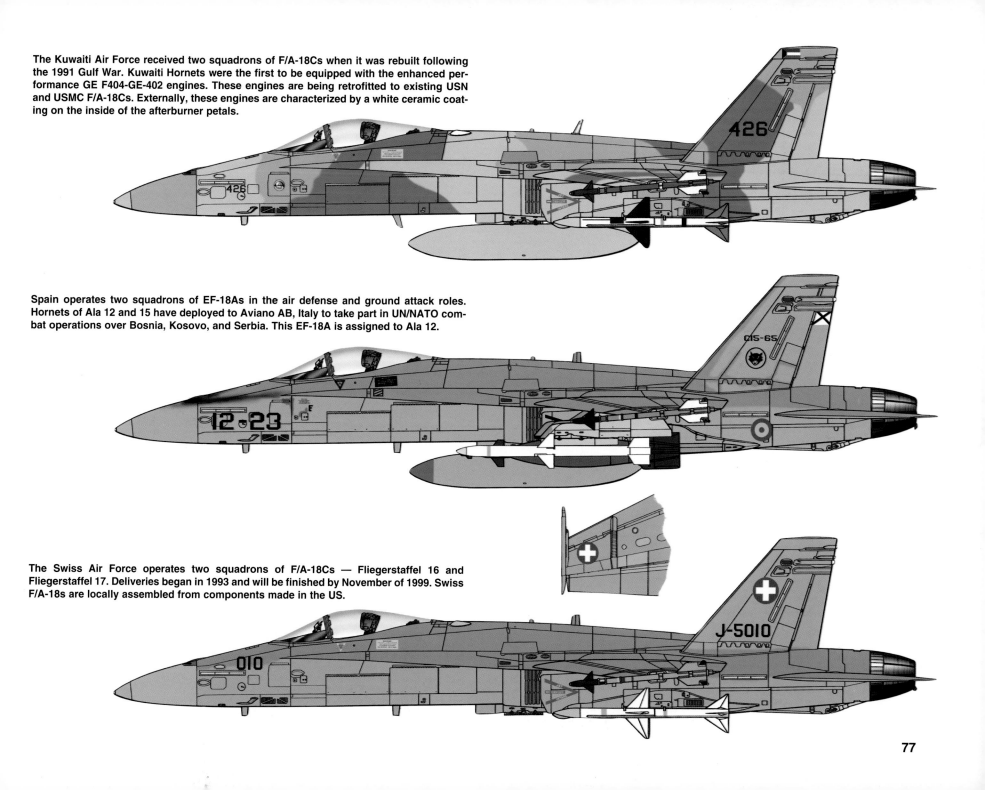

The Kuwaiti Air Force received two squadrons of F/A-18Cs when it was rebuilt following the 1991 Gulf War. Kuwaiti Hornets were the first to be equipped with the enhanced performance GE F404-GE-402 engines. These engines are being retrofitted to existing USN and USMC F/A-18Cs. Externally, these engines are characterized by a white ceramic coating on the inside of the afterburner petals.

Spain operates two squadrons of EF-18As in the air defense and ground attack roles. Hornets of Ala 12 and 15 have deployed to Aviano AB, Italy to take part in UN/NATO combat operations over Bosnia, Kosovo, and Serbia. This EF-18A is assigned to Ala 12.

The Swiss Air Force operates two squadrons of F/A-18Cs — Fliegerstaffel 16 and Fliegerstaffel 17. Deliveries began in 1993 and will be finished by November of 1999. Swiss F/A-18s are locally assembled from components made in the US.

The new Hornet retains the folding ladder under the port Leading Edge Extension to facilitate crew boarding. The single ladder serves both cockpits on the two seat F-18F. The wedge-shaped engine air intakes have been covered with a FOD screen to prevent debris from being ingested into the engines.

The LEXs and engine air intakes have been completely redesigned to improve aerodynamics and increase the flow of air into the GE F414 turbofan engines. The design is also believed to incorporate some stealth characteristics to lower the Hornet's radar signature.

The nose gear design emulates that of the earlier Hornets. Sawtooth edges have not been incorporated into the nose landing gear doors. The landing gear struts and wheel wells are painted gloss white. This single-seat F-18E is equipped with an internal 20mm gun.

The enlarged Leading Edge Extensions no longer require a LEX fence on the upper surface. The Super Hornet can fire the radar-guided AIM-120 AMRAAM (Advanced Medium Range Air-to-Air Missile) in addition to the AIM-7 Sparrow and AIM-9 Sidewinder missiles used on the previous Hornets. An inert AIM-9 Sidewinder is mounted on the port wingtip missile rail.

USMC Hornet pilots wear a one piece fire resistant NOMEX flight suit, NOMEX gloves, and hard leather flying boots. A partial G-suit, known as speed jeans, is worn around the waist and legs. The ensemble is completed by a survival vest, a deflated life preserver, and his seat/parachute harness. On combat missions, the pilot is also provided with a weapon, and all patches are removed from his flight suit — a process known as sanitization.

His external walk around completed, a suited and geared up US Marine Corps pilot is ready to start his cockpit checks and go fly. The flying helmet is covered with a cloth woodland camouflage cover to improve concealment in the event the pilot is forced down in enemy territory. Desert camouflage covers are also available. Semper Fi.

More modern fighters and bombers from squadron/signal publications

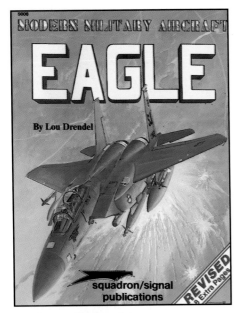

5008 F-15 Eagle

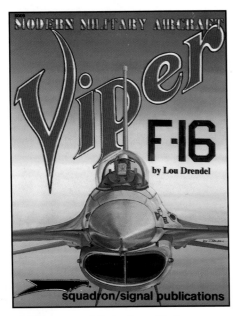

5009 F-16 Fighting Falcon

1105 F-14 Tomcat

1115 F-117 Stealth Fighter

1130 B-52 Stratofortress

5502 A-6 Intruder

5503 F-14 Tomcat

5517 A-10 Warthog